Maths Made Easy

by KATHLEEN PATERSON

WORKSHEETS
Book 3

EGON PUBLISHERS LTD.
618 Leeds Road, Outwood, Wakefield, WF1 2LT

First published in the United Kingdom in 1996
by Egon Publishers Ltd
618 Leeds Road, Outwood, Wakefield WF1 2LT

Maths Made Easy
Worksheet Book 3

This book was designed and compiled by Kathleen Paterson, Rosalind Birkett and Rachael Anderson who have many years of experience in the teaching of Primary School Mathematics.

The characters in Maths Made Easy are introduced at the beginning of the book. The aim has been to produce sheets which the children can work through independently and that are clear, simple and attractive. Children are allowed to gain numeracy without this being complicated by problems of layout and copying. The book can be worked through as a scheme in its own right or teachers may simply select particular sheets in order to reinforce other work.

The work includes the level of numeracy required by the National Curriculum Key Stage 1 Years 1 and 2 and covers Attainment Targets 1 and 2 and levels 1 and 2. The book is designed to give further practice in the understanding of place value, to introduce the learning of tens and units in logical stages and to cover the processes of carrying in addition and decomposition in subtraction. It is important that the pupils gain practical experience and therefore the sheets should be used in conjunction with tens and units apparatus. It is recommended that each child be provided with a minimum of 10 x 10 sticks and 20 x 1 unit bricks.

Egon also sells the Tens and Units house which is useful to explain sums involving tens and units in a visually and tactile way. It is important for children to use the house at each stage of learning as a practical method of increasing the child's understanding of the processes involved.

Contents

Meet More Pals

Duck

Moon

Spacephant

Fish

Featherbrain

ten and unit

Snail

Whale

Octopus

Name	Date	1

Tum finds it hard to add up big numbers but ten and unit help him. They put the bricks in their houses.

Tum always adds the units first then the tens.

		t	u
36		3	6
23	+	2	3

Remember – add the units first

		t	u
45		4	5
32	+	3	2

We can help you to add big numbers!

REMEMBER – Add the units first

			t	u
24			2	4
35		+	3	5

REMEMBER – Add the units first

		t	u
81			
16			

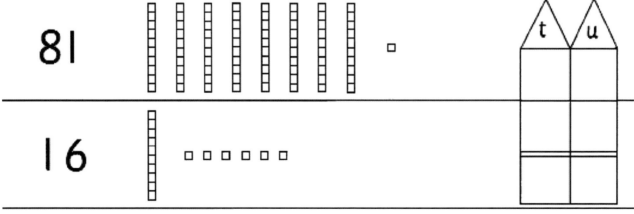

We can do them

Name	Date	3

REMEMBER – Always add the units first

---

62 + 24

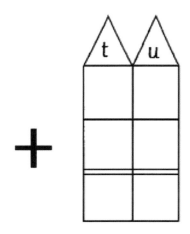

$+$

t	u
6	2
2	4

73 + 26

$+$

t	u

---

43 + 15

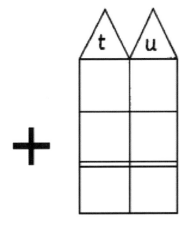

$+$

t	u

32 + 55

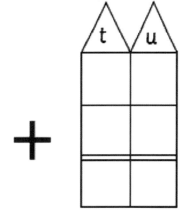

$+$

t	u

Name	Date	4

REMEMBER!  Add the units first

14 + 25=

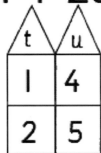

t	u
1	4
2	5

+

74 + 3=

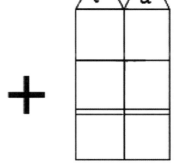

+

46 + 12=

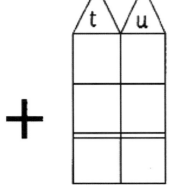

+

5 + 92=

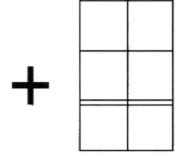

+

9 + 40=

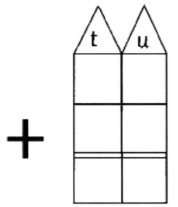

+

70 + 28=

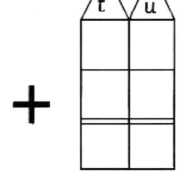

+

| Name | Date | 5 |

REMEMBER!  Add the units first!

---

23 + 44 =

```
  t  u
  2  3
+ 4  4
_____

_____
```

51 + 7 =

```
  t  u
  5  1
+    7
_____

_____
```

65 + 13 =

```
  t  u
  6  5
+ 1  3
_____

_____
```

---

3 + 42 =

```
  t  u

+
_____

_____
```

40 + 26 =

```
  t  u

+
_____

_____
```

31 + 13 =

```
  t  u

+
_____

_____
```

---

18 + 21 =

```
  t  u

+
_____

_____
```

62 + 6 =

```
  t  u

+
_____

_____
```

5 + 62 =

```
  t  u

+
_____

_____
```

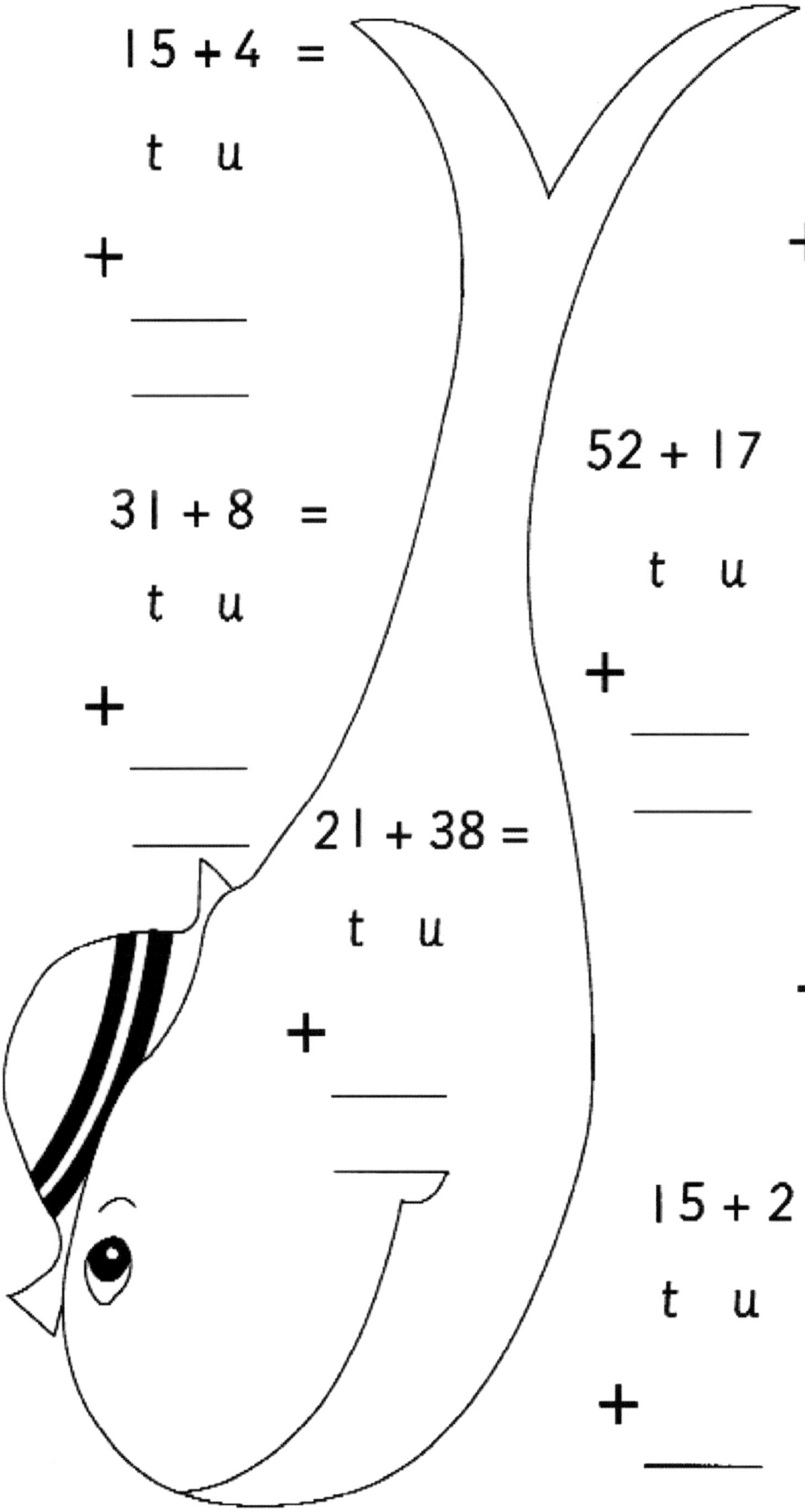

15 + 4 =

t   u

\+

_____

_____

31 + 8 =

t   u

\+

_____

_____

21 + 38 =

t   u

\+

_____

27 + 0 =

t   u

\+

_____

_____

52 + 17 =

t   u

\+

_____

_____

27 + 12 =

t   u

\+

_____

_____

15 + 21 =

t   u

\+

_____

_____

46 + 21 =
  t u

+

_____

_____

52 + 17 =
  t u

+

_____

_____

10 + 35 =
  t u

+

_____

_____

32 + 5 =
  t u

+

_____

_____

70 + 6 =
  t u

+

_____

_____

43 + 12 =
  t u

+

_____

_____

54 + 10 =
t   u

\+

_____

_____

28 + 30 =
t   u

\+

_____

_____

72 + 21 =
t   u

\+

_____

_____

4 + 25 =
t   u

\+

_____

_____

63 + 15 =
t   u

\+

_____

_____

53 + 7 =
t   u

\+

_____

_____

82 + 4 =
t   u

\+

_____

_____

21 + 3 =
t   u

\+

_____

_____

Help the moon to count the stars!

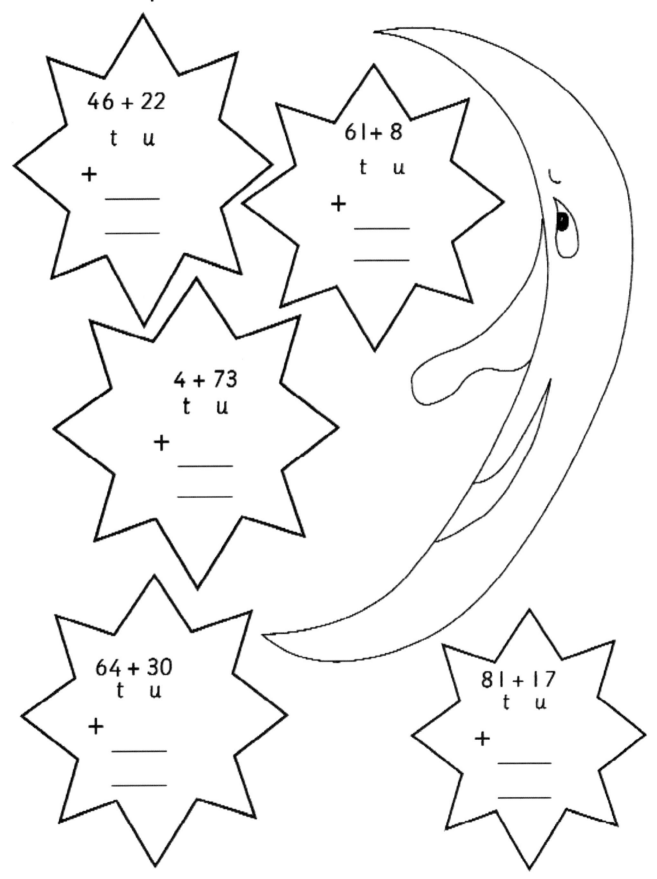

46 + 22
t   u

+

_____

_____

61 + 8
t   u

+

_____

_____

4 + 73
t   u

+

_____

_____

64 + 30
t   u

+

_____

_____

81 + 17
t   u

+

_____

_____

t	u	+	t	u	=	t	u
1	0	+	1	0	=	2	0
1	4	+	1	0	=	2	4
2	6	+	1	0	=		
3	8	+	1	0	=		
4	7	+	1	0	=		
5	3	+	1	0	=		
6	2	+	1	0	=		
7	1	+	1	0	=		

Did you notice that the units stay the same?

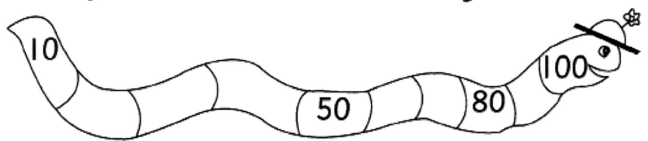

count in tens to 100.

Name	Date		1 1

Add the units to the units

t	u	+	t	u	=	t	u
2	0	+		4	=	2	4
3	0	+		7	=		
4	0	+		8	=		
5	0	+		5	=		
6	0	+		3	=		
7	0	+		2	=		
8	0	+		1	=		
9	0	+		9	=		

Did you notice that the tens stay the same?

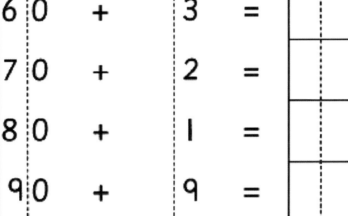

4 tens and 3 units = ☐
8 tens and 7 units = ☐
0 tens and 4 units = ☐

Fill in the missing numbers. Colour the 10s.

1	2		4					9	
11				15			18		
21		23			26				30
	32					37			
41				45					50
		53						59	
	62				66				
71			74				78		
		83				87			90
91								99	

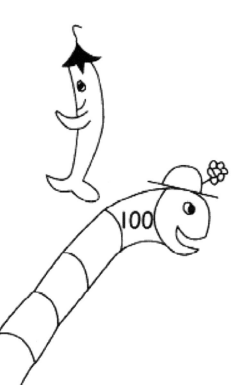

Count on in 10s

100
50
10

10 + 10 + 10 = ☐

20 + 10 + 10 = ☐

30 + 10 + 10 = ☐

40 + 10 + 10 = ☐

50 + 10 + 10 = ☐

90 − 10 = ☐

80 − 10 = ☐

70 − 10 = ☐

60 − 10 = ☐

50 − 10 = ☐

Count back from 100 on the square.

									10
									50
								69	70
71								79	
81							88		90
91								99	100 |←Start

Count in 10s ⟶

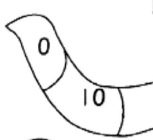

0

10

50

Count back from 100 ⟵

100

Count on from 50 ⟶

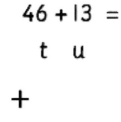

50

51 52

46 + 13 =	20 + 7 =	91+ 8 =	37 + 51 =	42 + 25 =
t u	t u	t u	t u	t u
+	+	+	+	+
___	___	___	___	___
___	___	___	___	___

| Name | Date | 14 |

tens and units

□ □ = □

tens and units

□ □ = □

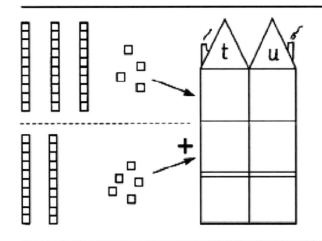 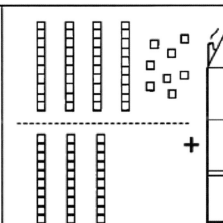

38 + 11 =	3 + 44 =	25 + 3 =	75 + 14 =	82 + 6 =
t u	t u	t u	t u	t u
+	+	+	+	+
___	___	___	___	___
___	___	___	___	___

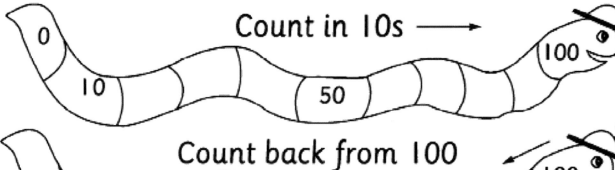

Count in 10s ⟶

Count back from 100

10 + 10 + 10 = □   30 + 10 + 10 = □

Name	Date	15

Fill in the missing numbers.
Count back from 80

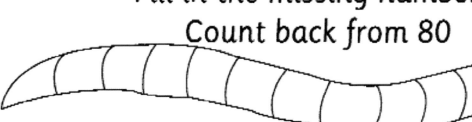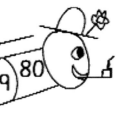

79 | 80

Count back from 100

99 | 100

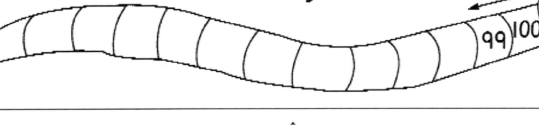

72 − 5 = ☐

81 − 4 = ☐

53 − 6 = ☐

43 − 7 = ☐

94 − 8 = ☐

90

80

17 − 10 = ☐

16 − 6 = ☐

14 − 10 = ☐

13 − 3 = ☐

18 − 10 = ☐

46 + 13 = t u + ___ ___	39 + 10 = t u + ___ ___	2 + 46 = t u + ___ ___	57 + 2 = t u + ___ ___

Tum finds it hard to take away big numbers but ten and unit help him. They put the biggest number upstairs in their houses.

Tum takes away the units first

78 – 43 (cross out 43)

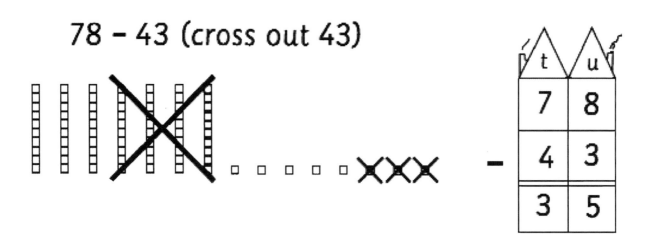

REMEMBER – take away the units first

97 – 54 (cross out 54)

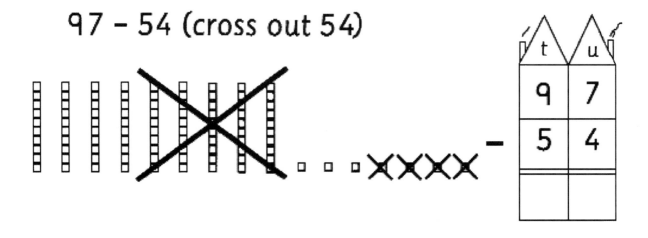

REMEMBER – take away the units first

49 – 26 (cross out 26)

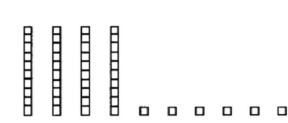

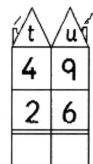

We can help you take away big numbers !

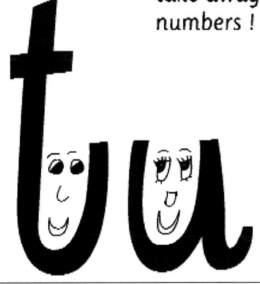

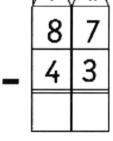

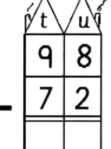

36 –14 (cross out 14)

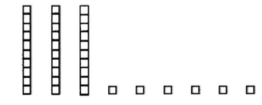

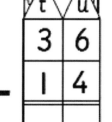

54 – 20 (cross out 20)

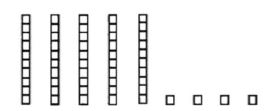

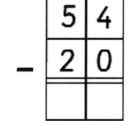

Name	Date	18

REMEMBER – Units first!

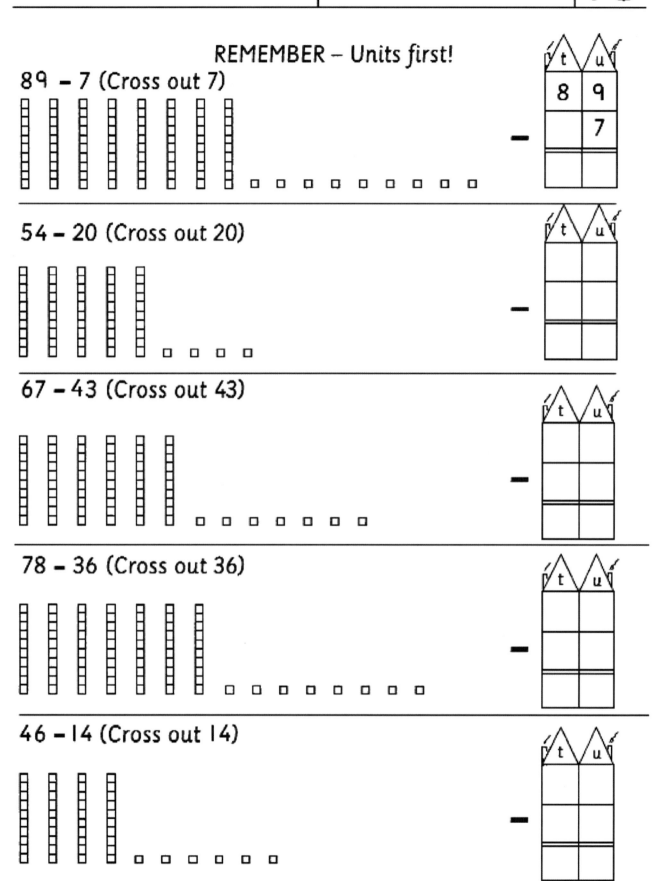

89 – 7 (Cross out 7)

54 – 20 (Cross out 20)

67 – 43 (Cross out 43)

78 – 36 (Cross out 36)

46 – 14 (Cross out 14)

REMEMBER – Units first!

Name | Date   19

Pod needs to drive the car back to the right house. Can you
help him? Draw a line from the car to the right house.

t	u
8	6
1	4

t	u
7	9
4	3

t	u
9	5
5	2

23

t	u
6	7
2	5

t	u
5	8
2	0

t	u
7	4
5	3

t	u
4	7
	5

t	u
8	9
6	3

t	u
3	5
1	2

Name	Date	20

Find each fruit a bowl
to go in. Draw a line
to the correct
fruit bowl.

```
  t  u
  4  8
- 2  6
_____
```

31

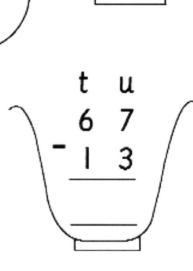

```
  t  u
  6  7
- 1  3
_____
```

22

```
  t  u
  7  6
- 4  5
_____
```

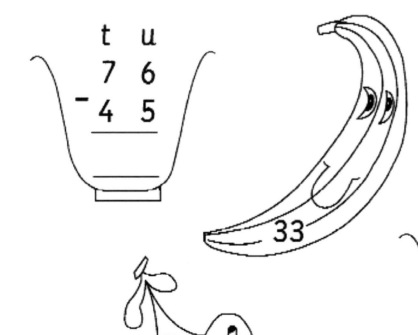

33

```
  t  u
  9  5
- 6  2
_____
```

54

Colour the clothes that match the man's jumper

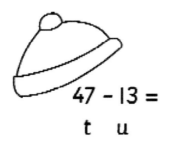

47 – 13 =
t   u

–
_____

68 – 7 =
t   u

–
_____

_____

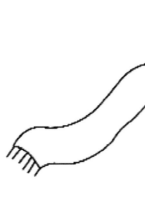

21

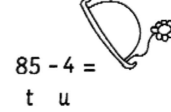

85 – 4 =
t   u

–
_____

_____

98 – 26 =
t   u

–
_____

_____

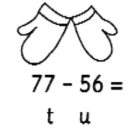

77 – 56 =
t   u

–
_____

_____

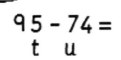

95 – 74 =
t   u

–
_____

_____

49 – 17 =
t   u

–
_____

_____

Name	Date	22

Help Featherbrain to do his sums!

46 – 22

t u

−
___
___

87 – 63

t u

−
___
___

59 – 26

t u

−
___
___

97 – 64

t u

−
___
___

74 – 20

t u

−
___
___

85 – 61

t u

−
___
___

65 – 14

t u

−
___
___

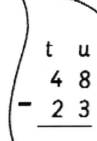

```
  t  u
  4  8
- 2  3
_____
```

```
  t  u
  6  4
- 2  0
_____
```

```
  t  u
  2  5
- 1  4
_____
```

```
  t  u
  9  7
- 6  2
_____
```

```
  t  u        t  u        t  u
  7  6        8  6        6  5
- 3  4      - 4  3      - 2  3
_____      _____      _____
```

Count
down

100

99

98

Count
down
in 10s

100

90

80

Name	Date	24

Pod looks at the signs so he gets home safely!

48 + 20	76 − 42	23 + 6
t u	t u	t u
+ ___	− ___	+ ___
___	___	___

98 − 56	33 + 45	79 − 50
t u	t u	t u
− ___	+ ___	− ___
___	___	___

13 + 24	87 − 4	52 + 7
t u	t u	t u
+ ___	− ___	+ ___
___	___	___

| Name | Date | 25 |

Look at the sign ➕ or ➖

or you will  crash

42 + 23 t u ___ ___	67 – 43 t u ___ ___	25 + 4 t u ___ ___
86 – 43 t u ___ ___		97 – 14 t u ___ ___
34 + 25 t u ___ ___	79 – 5 t u ___ ___	81+ 10 t u ___ ___

| Name | Date | 26 |

Look at the sign ➕ or ➖

or you will  crash

27 + 42 t u ___ ___ ___ ___	78 – 36 t u ___ ___ ___ ___	58 – 7 t u ___ ___ ___ ___
2 + 47 t u ___ ___ ___ ___	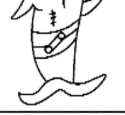	59 – 25 t u ___ ___ ___ ___
76 – 54 t u ___ ___ ___ ___	42 + 36 t u ___ ___ ___ ___	50 + 38 t u ___ ___ ___ ___

Name	Date	27

Tum can add up three
big numbers.
        Can you?

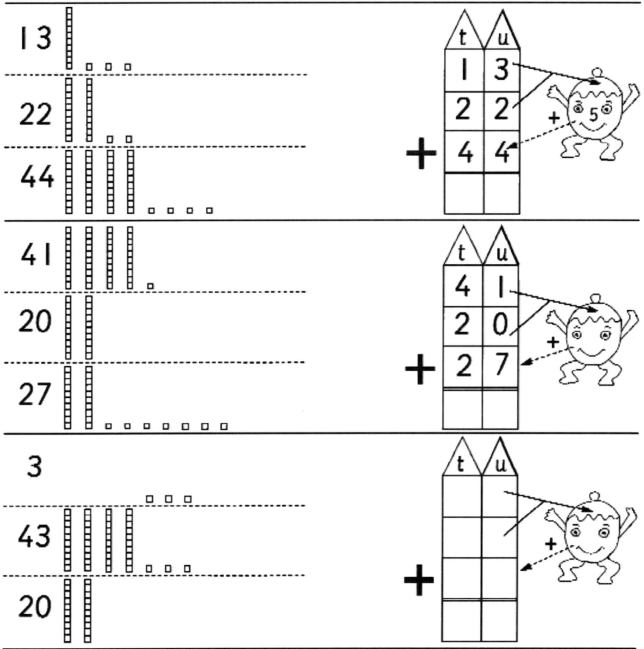

13

22

44

	t	u
	1	3
	2	2
+	4	4

+ 5

41

20

27

	t	u
	4	1
	2	0
+	2	7

3

43

20

	t	u
+		

REMEMBER – Add the units first!

Name	Date	28

Ted and Pot play bingo! Who wins?

3	76	64
26	5	85
23	15	58

Ted

78	29	30
95	7	36
51	13	47

Pot

Work out each answer to the sums. Then for each answer put an **X** on the players card that has that number. Begin at number 1. Whoever gets three **X**'s in a row wins!

1.

```
  t  u
  2  1
  1  3
+ 2  4
―――――
  5  8
```

2.

```
  t  u
  3  2
  1  6
+ 3  0
―――――
```

3.

```
  t  u
  1  0
  2  4
+ 1  3
―――――
```

4.

```
  t  u
  4  3
  1  2
+ 2  1
―――――
```

5.

```
  t  u
  7  9
- 5  6
―――――
```

6.

```
  t  u
  6  5
- 5  2
―――――
```

7.

```
  t  u
  5  9
- 5  4
―――――
```

8.

```
  t  u
  6  8
- 3  2
―――――
```

9.

```
  t  u
  1  3
+ 1  6
―――――
```

10.

```
  t  u
  2  4
+    2
―――――
```

11.

```
  t  u
  3  1
+ 6  4
―――――
```

12.

```
  t  u
  5  1
+ 3  4
―――――
```

A Story about 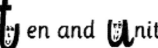 Ten and Unit

Ten and Unit are good pals.
They live next door to one another.
They both like to eat sweets!

Unit keeps her sweets on the shelf. She never keeps more than 9 on the shelf. If she has 10 she gets them together and puts them in packets of 10 on the doorstep of tens' house. She keeps the ones that she has left.

Ten is more greedy! He saves his sweets in packets of 10. He also keeps the packets of 10 that his pal gives him.

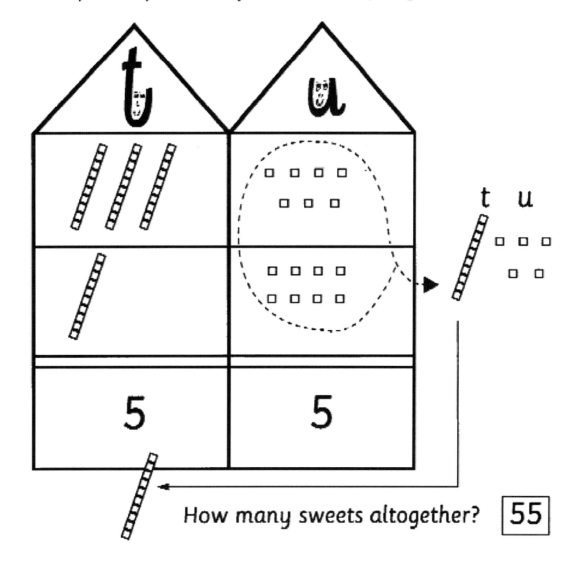

How many sweets altogether? 55

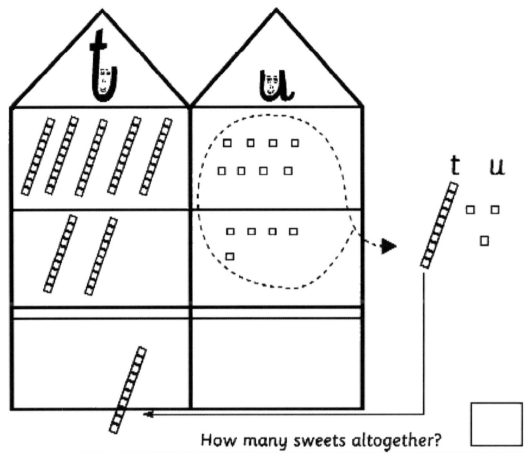

How many sweets altogether?

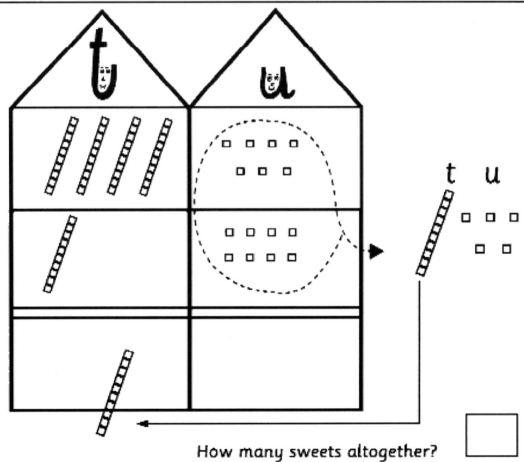

How many sweets altogether?

Help **t**en and **u**nit add up their sweets!

REMEMBER – Add the units first

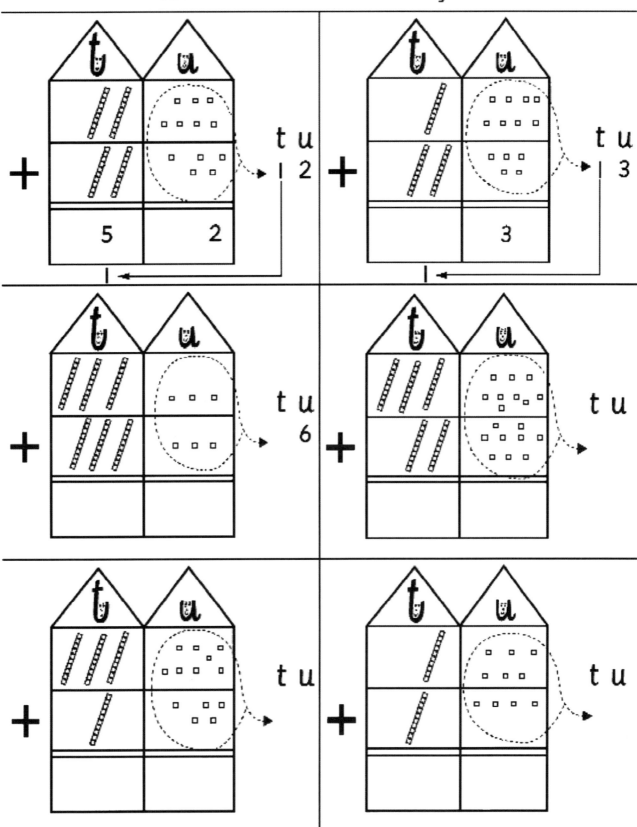

Name	Date	32

Help **t**en and **u**nit add up their sweets!

REMEMBER – Add the units first

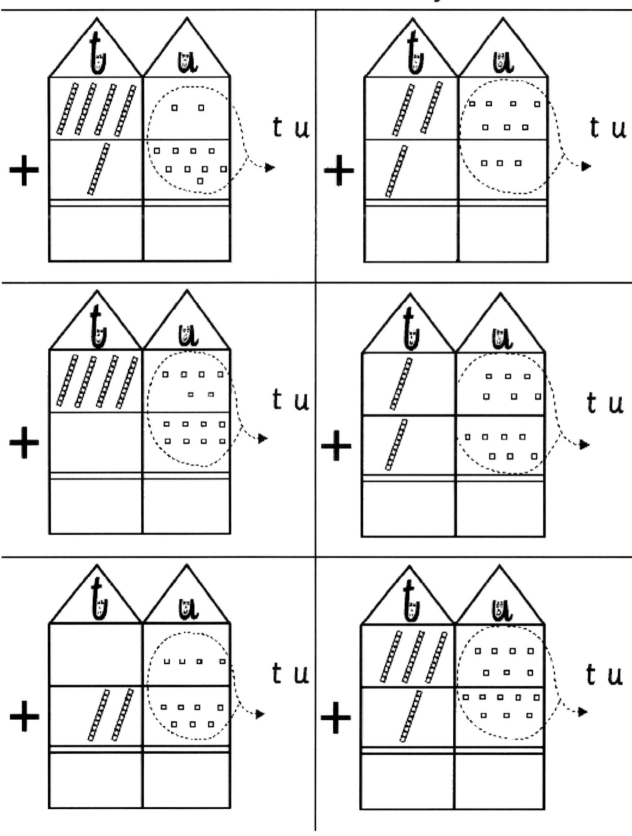

Name	Date	33

Help **t**en and **u**nit add up their sweets!

REMEMBER – Add the units first

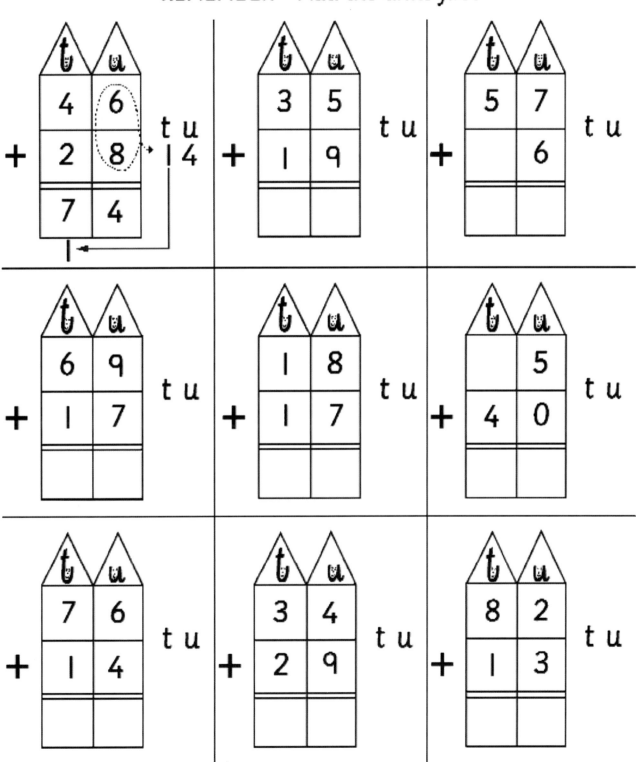

REMEMBER – Add the units first!

Name	Date	34

REMEMBER!  Add the units first!

28 + 17 =

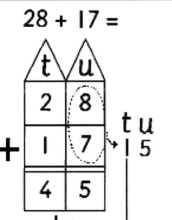

39 + 48 =

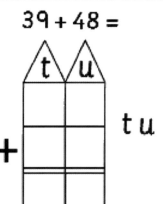

7 + 56 =

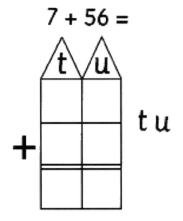

74 + 3 =

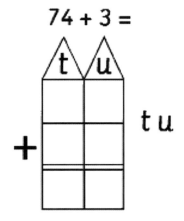

68 + 12 =

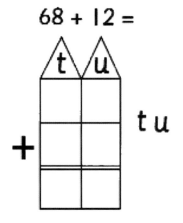

69 + 17 =

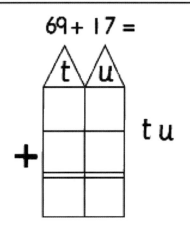

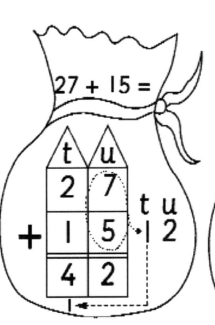

27 + 15 =

t	u
2	7
1	5
4	2

+

t u
1 2

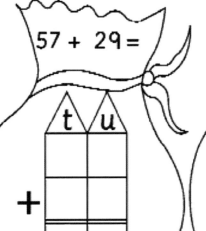

57 + 29 =

+

| t | u |

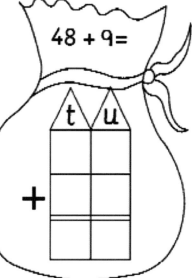

48 + 9=

+

| t | u |

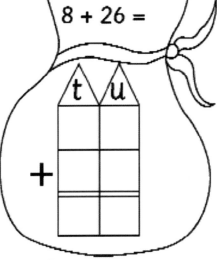

8 + 26 =

+

| t | u |

Work out the sums
to find how many
seeds Pot should
put in each bag?

REMEMBER
Add the units first!

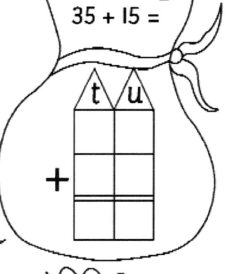

35 + 15 =

+

| t | u |

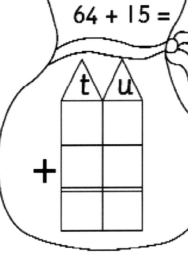

64 + 15 =

+

| t | u |

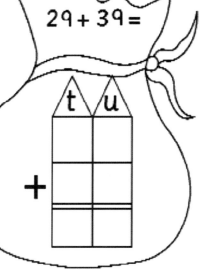

29 + 39=

+

| t | u |

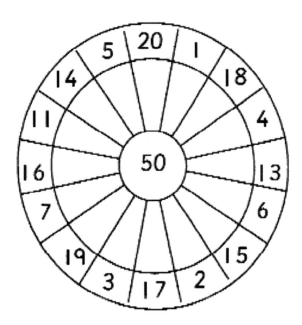

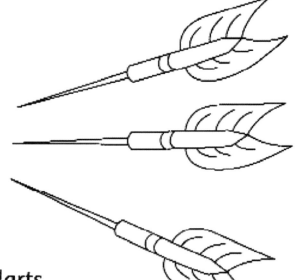

Pot, Pod and Tum each threw 3 darts.
Add up their scores. Who won?

Pot

(17) (19) (18)

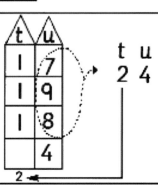

Pod

(20) (15) (16)

t u

Tum

(50) (18) (15)

t u

Dart Scores!

Pot

t	u
2	0
1	8
1	7

t u

+

Pod

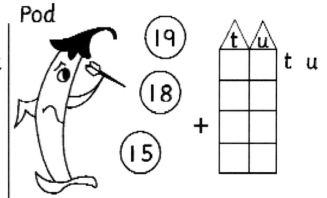

+

Tum

+

Drip

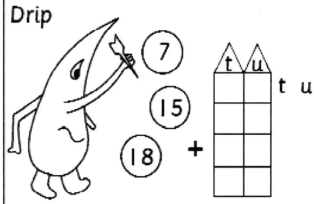

+

Man

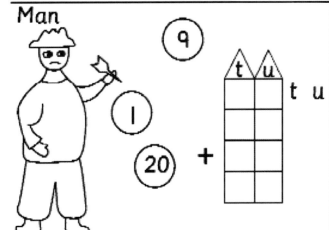

+

Bug

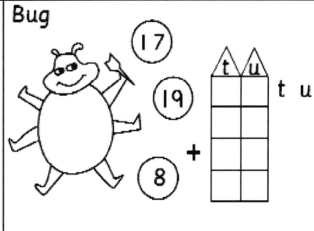

+

Who won the cup?

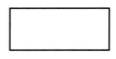

Put the scores in order. Start with the lowest.

Name	Date	38

Ted, Drip, Bug and the man each threw 3 hoops at the Hoop La!

Add up each of their scores. Who won?

Ted

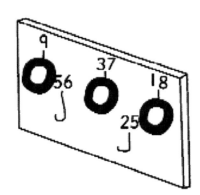

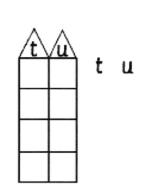

t	u		t	u
	9		2	4
3	7			
1	8			
6	4			

Drip

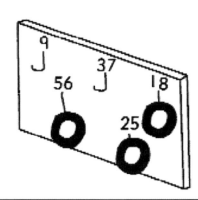

t	u		t	u

Bug

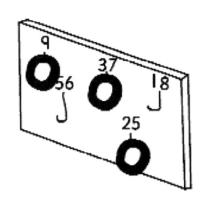

t	u		t	u

Man

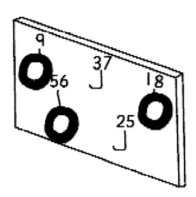

t	u		t	u

Name

Date

39

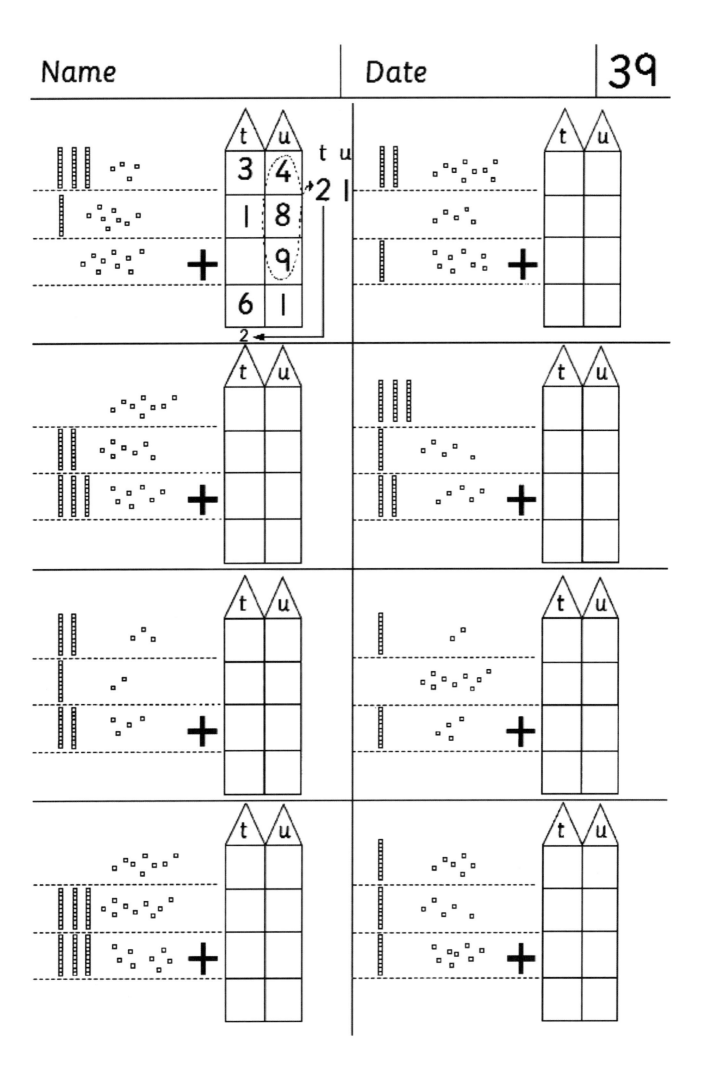

Name	Date	40

Windmill fun!

Fill in the missing numbers on the sails

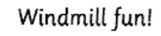

Numbers on the sails: 43, 100, 49, 50, 10, 57

Fill in the missing numbers on the roundhouse.

Tum wants to find out how many sacks are in the windmill. Can you help him?

Flour

```
  t  u
  1  9
  2  8
+ 4  6
-------
```

Pod is counting back. Can you help him?

100
99
98
97
96
95
94
93

Roundhouse numbers: 5, 10, 35

```
 t  u
 4  7
-2  5
-------
```

Tum wants 3 small sacks of flour. They cost 10p each. How much must he spend?

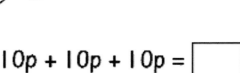

$10p + 10p + 10p = \boxed{}$

Name	Date	41

Join the dots from 1 – 60

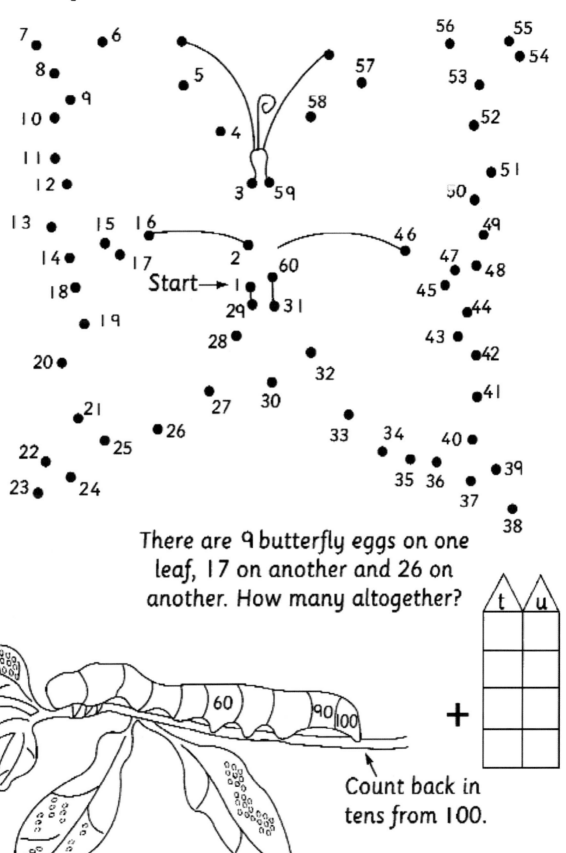

7 6
56 55
8 54
9 53
5 57
10 58
11 52
4
12 51
50
3 59
13 15 16 49
46
14 17 2 47 48
60
Start → 1 45
18 29 31 44
19 43
28 42
20
32 41
21 27 30
26 33 34 40
25 35 36 39
22 23 24 37 38

There are 9 butterfly eggs on one
leaf, 17 on another and 26 on
another. How many altogether?

60 90 100

+

Count back in
tens from 100.

t	u

Name	Date	42

Look at the sign **+** or **-**

or you will  crash

28 + 31 = t u ___ ___	85 - 63 = t u ___ ___	39 + 18 = t u ___ ___
69 - 45 = t u ___ ___	-REMEMBER- Units first! 	74 - 52 = t u ___ ___
18 + 7 + 36 = t u ___ ___	56 + 19 + 15 = t u ___ ___	34 + 26 + 8 = t u ___ ___

Unit is feeling hungry. She wants to eat 8 sweets. She looks upstairs on her shelf but finds that she only has 4 sweets.

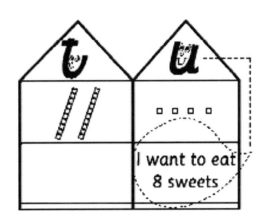

Unit cannot eat 8 sweets unless she asks

ten to give her one of his packets of 10.
He is kind and lets her have one of his packets of 10.

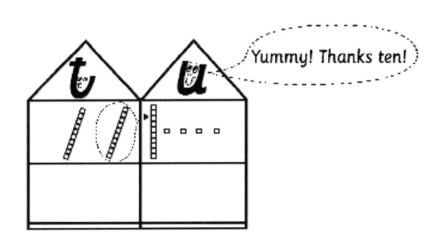

Unit unwraps the packet of ten. She now has 14 sweets.
She can now eat 8 sweets and has 6 left.

ten has one less packet of 10 sweets.

Name	Date	44

Can **t***u*nit eat 7 sweets without asking *t*en for one of his packets of 10?

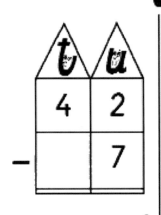

t	u
4	2
−	7

Yes | N̶o̶ ✓

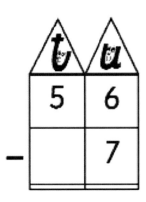

t	u
3	8
−	7

Yes ✓ | No

t	u
5	6
−	7

Yes | No

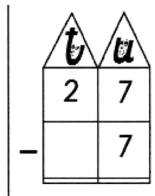

t	u
2	7
−	7

Yes | No

t	u
1	9
−	7

Yes | No

t	u
2	8
−	7

Yes | No

t	u
4	3
−	7

Yes | No

t	u
5	5
−	7

Yes | No

t	u
3	4
−	7

Yes | No

t	u
2	2
−	7

Yes | No

t	u
3	1
−	7

Yes | No

t	u
4	0
−	7

Yes | No

How many sweets do **t**en and **u**nit have left?

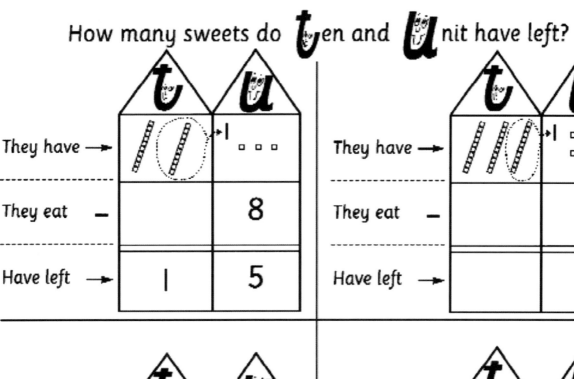

They have →
They eat −
Have left →

t	u
10	·1 □ □ □
	8
1	5

They have →
They eat −
Have left →

t	u
10	·1 □ □ □ □ □ □
	9

They have →
They eat −
Have left →

t	u
10	·1 □ □
	5

They have →
They eat −
Have left →

t	u
10	·1 □ □ □ □
	7

They have →
They eat −
Have left →

t	u
1	□ □ □ □ □ □ □ □
	6

They have →
They eat −
Have left →

t	u
10	·1 □ □ □ □ □ □ □
	8

How many sweets do en and nit have left?

Box 1 (top left):

t	u
//0 (crossed)	►1 ▫ ▫
They eat − 1	6
Have left →	

Box 2 (top right):

t	u
/0 (circled)	►1 ▫ ▫ ▫
They eat −	5
Have left →	

Box 3 (middle left):

t	u
1 2̸ ►1	3
They eat −	8
Have left → 1	5

Box 4 (middle right):

t	u
3 4̸ ►1	2
They eat − 1	5
Have left →	

Box 5 (bottom left):

t	u
6	4
They eat − 2	8
Have left →	

Box 6 (bottom right):

t	u
5	6
They eat − 3	9
Have left →	

Name	Date	47

How many sweets do 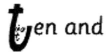en and Unit have left?

Box 1

	t	u
They have →	6̶7̶	¹2
They eat –	3	5
Have left →	3	7

Box 2

	t	u
They have →	7̶8̶	¹4
They eat –	2	6
Have left →		

Box 3

	t	u
They have →	8	3
They eat –	4	7
Have left →		

Box 4

	t	u
They have →	4	8
They eat –	2	4
Have left →		

Box 5

	t	u
They have →	6	5
They eat –	1	7
Have left →		

Box 6

	t	u
They have →	3	6
They eat –		9
Have left →		

Box 7

	t	u
They have →	5	7
They eat –	2	4
Have left →		

Box 8

	t	u
They have →	9	1
They eat –	7	8
Have left →		

| Name | Date | 48 |

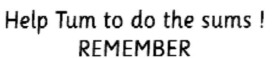

Help Tum to do the sums !
REMEMBER
Take away the units first
You cannot take the top line from the bottom one.

43 - 29 =	32 - 8 =	91 - 46 =
t u	t u	t u
³4̷ ¹3		
- 2 9	___	___
1 4		
	___	___

77 - 35 =	54 - 18 =	39 - 19 =
t u	t u	t u
___	___	___
___	___	___

45 - 27 =	67 - 29 =	34 - 7 =
t u	t u	t u
___	___	___
___	___	___

| Name | Date | 49 |

Help the fish to find out how many are left !

96 – 48 =
t   u

-
_____

84 – 27 =
t   u

-
_____

_____

44

50

51

66

71

72

29 –   8 =
t   u

-
_____

_____

46 – 19=
t   u

-
_____

_____

26

30

65 – 18 =
t   u

-
_____

_____

Put the missing numbers in
the bubbles

Duck ate some pieces of bread. Help him to
work out how many pieces of bread he has left.

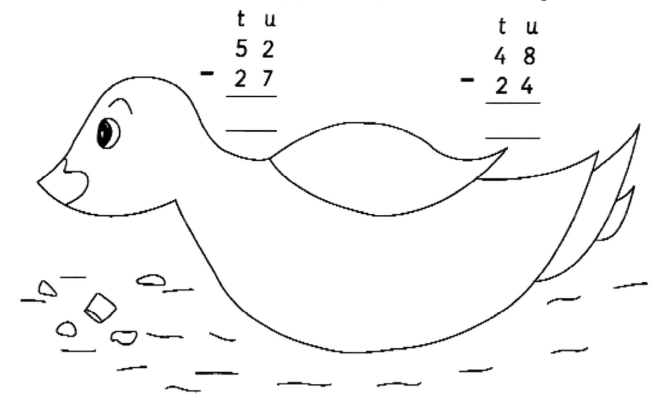

```
  t  u              t  u
  5  2              4  8
- 2  7            - 2  4
 ─────             ─────
```

43 − 7 =	51 − 35 =	97 − 43 =
t u	t u	t u
- ──	- ──	- ──
──	──	──

75 − 35 =	68 − 34 =	84 − 57 =
t u	t u	t u
- ──	- ──	- ──
──	──	──

Name	Date	51

Octopus eats some fish. Help him to work out how many are left.

```
        t u          t u
        9 3          6 1
      - 5 6        - 4 3
      -------      -------
```

```
        t u
        8 6
      - 5 7
      -------
```

```
        t u
        5 8
      - 2 6
      -------
```

```
    t u          t u
    6 5          7 2
  - 2 5        - 3 8
  -------      -------
```

```
    t u          t u          t u
    8 0          4 9          6 4
  - 4 7        - 2 6        - 2 8
  -------      -------      -------
```

= ☐ |||| ⬜ = ☐

Count in 10s to 100

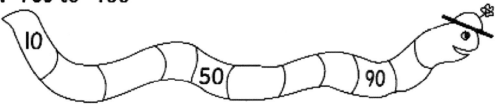

Fill in the missing numbers.

☐ + 6 = 16   5 + ☐ = 15

8 + ☐ = 20   13 + 7 = ☐

5 + ☐ = 20   13 - 7 = ☐

☐ + 10 = 19   13 + ☐ = 20

76 - 42 =	29 + 37 =	92 - 46 =	34 + 25 =
t u	t u	t u	t u
___	___	___	___
___	___	___	___

7 + 18 + 29 =   Look at the sign + or –   19 + 26 + 45 =

t u   or you will crash!   t u

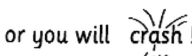

___   ___

___   ___

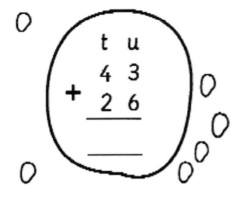

```
      t  u
      4  3
  +   2  6
  _____

```

```
      t  u
      5  8
  -   1  3
  _____
```

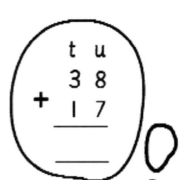

```
      t  u
      3  8
  +   1  7
  _____
```

Help Fish to count the bubbles !

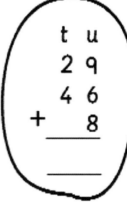

```
      t  u
      2  9
      4  6
  +      8
  _____
```

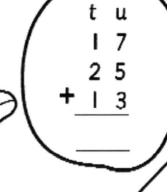

```
      t  u
      7  5
  -   1  6
  _____
```

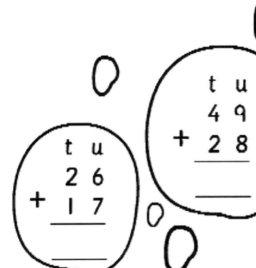

```
      t  u
      4  9
  +   2  8
  _____
```

```
      t  u
      2  6
  +   1  7
  _____
```

```
      t  u
      1  7
      2  5
  +   1  3
  _____
```

Snail cannot remember how to do these sums!
Can you help him ?

$10 + 10 + 10 + 10 =$ ☐

$38 - 15 =$
t   u

$46 + 24 =$
t   u

_____

_____

_____

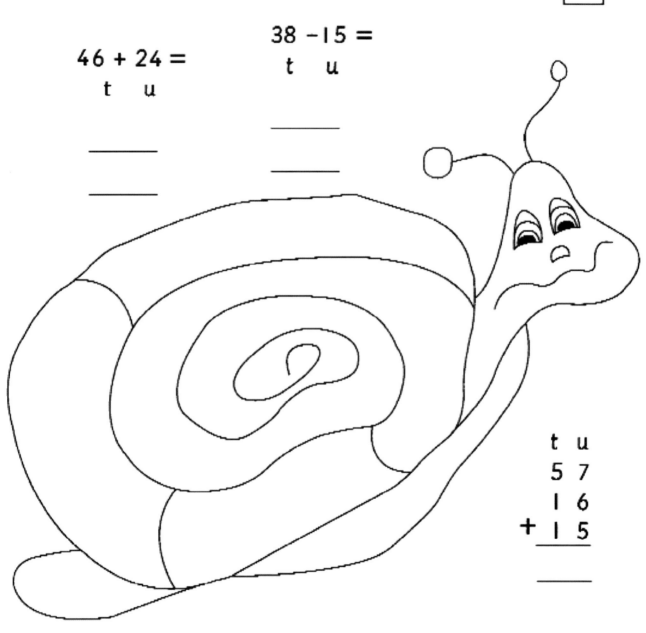

```
   t u
   5 7
   1 6
 + 1 5
 _____
```

$92 - 46 =$
t   u

$83 - 45 =$
t   u

$28 + 9 =$
t   u

_____

_____

_____

_____

_____

_____

Name	Date	55

Write the next number.

14		1 1		19		29		20	

Write the number which comes first.

	13		20		14		12		21

Colour the bigger number.

21	12		23	32		14	41		19	16		13	31

Colour the smaller number.

15	13		12	21		20	12		24	42		18	80

42 + 35 =	78 - 14 =	28 + 37 =	46 - 19 =
t u	t u	t u	t u
——	——	——	——
——	——	——	——

2 tens and 5 units = ☐   24 = ☐ tens and ☐ units

0 tens and 4 units = ☐   6 = ☐ tens and ☐ units

3 tens and 0 units = ☐   50 = ☐ tens and ☐ units

Spacephant sends a message in secret code to his pals on earth !

Work out the sums below, to find the message. Start at 1.

This is the secret code.

a	b	c	d	e	f	g	h	i	j	k	l	m
2	4	6	8	10	12	14	16	18	20	22	24	26

n	o	p	q	r	s	t	u	v	w	x	y	z
28	30	32	34	36	38	40	42	44	46	48	50	52

1.
```
    t u
  ³⁄4 ¹3
 -  2 9
   ‾‾‾‾
    1 4
```

2.
```
    t u
    1 9
 +  1 7
   ‾‾‾‾
```

3.
```
    t u
    4 0
 -  3 0
   ‾‾‾‾
```

4.
```
    t u
    5 7
 -  4 7
   ‾‾‾‾
```

5. 30 + 10 = ☐

6. 24 - 6 = ☐

7. 32 - 4 = ☐

8. 7 + 7 = ☐

9. 46 - 8 = ☐

10. 14 - 4 = ☐

11. 12 - 10 = ☐

12. 30 + 6 = ☐

13. 50 - 10 = ☐

14. 20 - 4 = ☐

15. 30 - 6 = ☐

16. 25 - 7 = ☐

17. 36 - 8 = ☐

18. 21 - 7 = ☐

19. 32 + 6 = ☐

The message says:-

1	2	3	4	5	6	7	8	9
14								
g								

10	11	12	13	14	15	16	17	18	19

The pals sent a mesage back to Spacephant !
They used the same code.

a	b	c	d	e	f	g	h	i	j	k	l	m
2	4	6	8	10	12	14	16	18	20	22	24	26

n	o	p	q	r	s	t	u	v	w	x	y	z
28	30	32	34	36	38	40	42	44	46	48	50	52

Work out the sums below to find out what they said>
Start at 1.

1. $16 - 10 = \boxed{}$

2. $20 + 10 = \boxed{}$

3. $36 - 10 = \boxed{}$

4. $20 - 10 = \boxed{}$

5. $12 - 10 = \boxed{}$

6. $38 - 10 = \boxed{}$

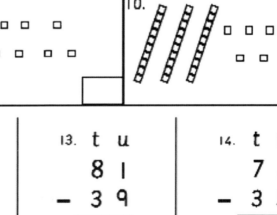

7.

8.

9.

10.

11.
```
  t u
    9
    5
+   4
_____
```

12.
```
  t u
  1 6
  1 3
+ 1 1
_____
```

13.
```
  t u
  8 1
- 3 9
_____
```

14.
```
  t u
  7 3
- 3 5
_____
```

The message says:-

1	2	3	4

5	6	7

8	9	10	11	12

13	14

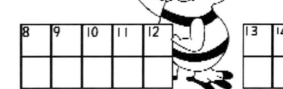

Name	Date	58

These words and sign tell you to add:-

add – addition

total.

plus

Find the sum of...

Find the total of...

What is the sum of...?

What is the total of...?

How many altogether?

---

1. Find the total of 6, 8 and 4. ☐

2. Add together 38 and 7. ☐

3. What is the sum of 9, 3 and 5?. ☐

4. Total these numbers. 10, 4 and 6. ☐

5. What is the total of 25 and 9 ? ☐

6. Find the sum of 68 and 7. ☐

7. Pod has 6 sweets. Ted has 7 sweets. ☐
   How many did they have altogether?

Name	Date	59

These words and sign tell you to take away:-

subtract

minus

How many left ?

take away

What is the difference ?

Find the difference ?

How many more ?

1. Take away 5 from 9. ☐

2. Subtract 3 from 41. ☐

3. Ted had 18 sweets. He gave away 5. How many did he have left ? ☐

4. What is the difference between 15 and 9 ? ☐

5. 32 minus 9 = ☐

6. Find the difference between 17 and 8. ☐

7. How many more is 20 than 15 ? ☐

Find the difference

 Pot has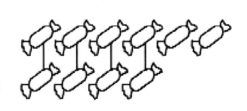

$$\begin{array}{c} 6 \\ - 4 \\ \hline 2 \end{array}$$ sweets
sweets

Pod has

Pot has | 2 | more sweets than Pod.
The difference between them is | 2 |

 Tum has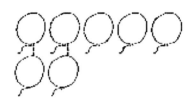

$$\begin{array}{c} 5 \\ - 2 \\ \hline \end{array}$$ balloons
balloons

Drip has

Tum has| | more balloons than Drip.
The difference between them is | |

Ted has ●●●●●●●●●●●●

Bug has ●●●●●

	t	u	
	I	I	marbles
−		5	marbles

Ted has | | more marbles than Bug.
The difference between them is | |

Find the difference

Fish has ⌇⌇⌇⌇⌇⌇⌇⌇⌇⌇⌇⌇⌇⌇

Octopus has ⌇⌇⌇⌇⌇⌇⌇

t	u
		hats
		hats

−

Fish has ☐ more hats than Octopus.
The difference between them is ☐

Moon sees ✿✿   ☐ flowers

Sun sees ✿✿✿✿✿✿✿✿   ☐ flowers

☐ − ☐ = ☐

Sun sees ☐ more flowers than Moon.
The difference between them is ☐

Blip has ✦✦✦✦✦✦   ☐ kites

Worm has ✦✦✦✦✦✦✦✦   ☐ kites

☐ − ☐ = ☐

Worm has ☐ more kites than Blip.
The difference between them is ☐

Find the difference

REMEMBER – To find the difference you must take away.
– Always put the biggest number on the top line.

Find the difference between

25 and 33	45 and 24	36 and 49	23 and 46
t u	t u	t u	t u
− ___	− ___	− ___	− ___
___	___	___	___

What is the difference between 46 and 8 ☐

Find the difference between 9 and 15 ☐

Pod dropped 12 pencils but Drip picked
up 6. How many pencils were left ? ☐

Pot had 18 seeds. He gave 6 to Tum.
How many more did Pot have than Tum ? ☐

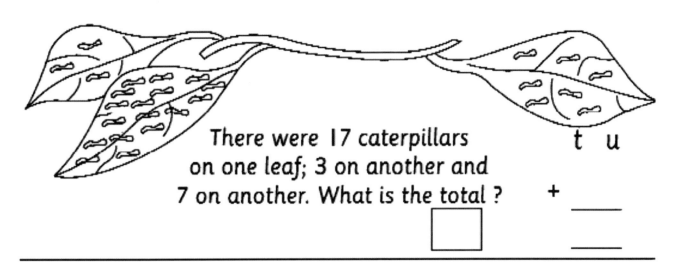

There were 17 caterpillars
on one leaf; 3 on another and
7 on another. What is the total ?

t   u

+ ____
____

Pot had 15 apples. He ate 5.
How many were left ?

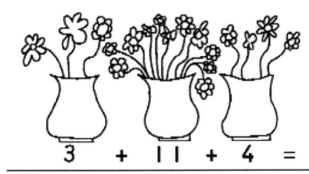

There were 3 flowers in one vase;
11 flowers in another and 4 in
another. How many altogether ?

3   +   11   +   4   =

There were 28 ducks on
the pond; 9 swam away.
How many were left ?

t   u

- ____
____

Using a Tens and Units house

The Tens and Units house is a teacher's aid and should be used with tens and units apparatus. Used properly it helps the teacher to explain tens and units sums visually. The teacher can insert tens and units bricks from the back and the children are able to see them at the front. Children can play with the house themselves, thinking up their own sums and showing one another.

The house is designed to look like a tens and units sum and, having used it, children seem to have less difficulty with the layout of their work. It is particularly valuable for children with visual learning difficulties.

The house can be used to demonstrate simple addition without carrying. It has a "doorstep" so that the teacher can demonstrate carrying a ten and putting it on the doorstep of the Tens section of the house.

In subtraction the idea of having a certain number of sweets or bricks on the shelf upstairs can be demonstrated. This helps children to understand that you can only take away at most what you have on the top line. The understanding of decomposition is also helped by seeing the process demonstrated.

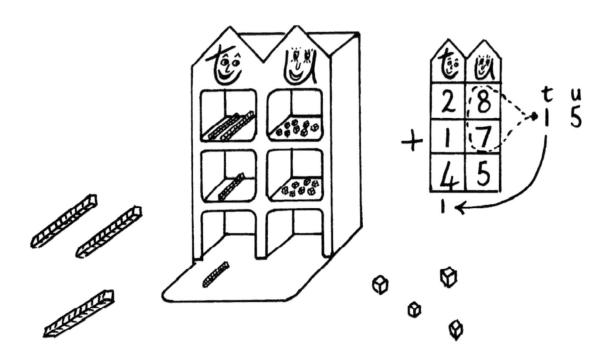

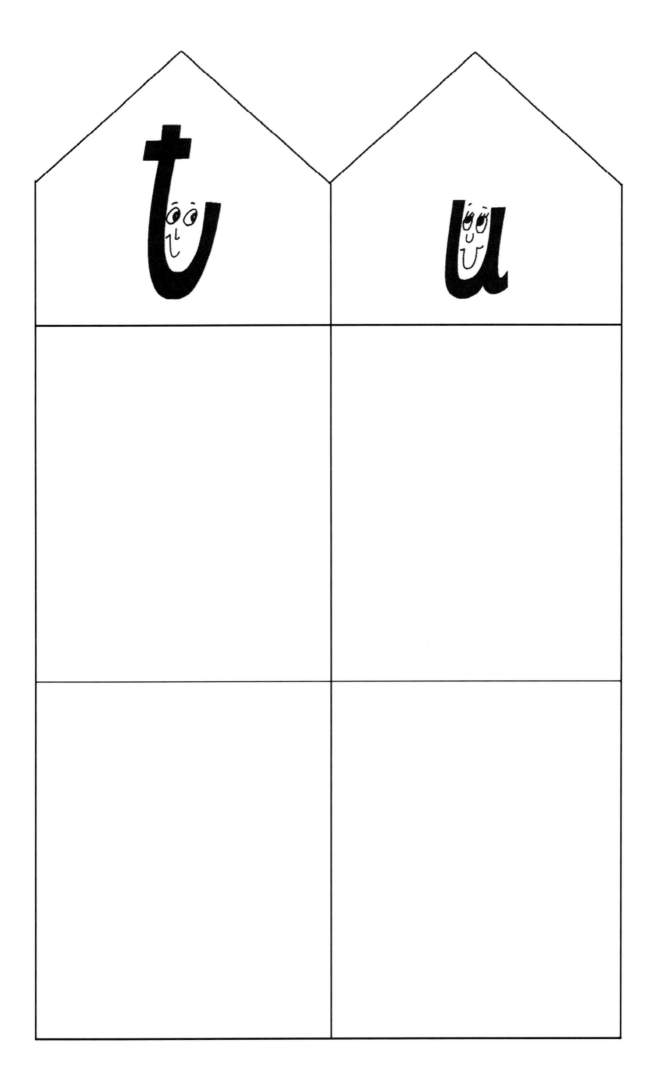